Yes, Virginia

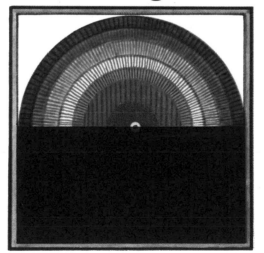

Yes, Virginia

ILLUSTRATED
BY
SUZANNE
HAUSMAN

ELIZABETH
PRESS
NEW YORK,
NEW YORK

To All the Virginias

Yes, Virginia was a real little girl and her story actually happened. In the fall of 1897, Virginia O'Hanlon wrote a letter to the editor of a New York newspaper asking "Is there a Santa Claus?" The letter and the response became hallmarks of the spirit and reality of Christmas. Virginia was eight years old.

The first twinges of doubt had begun to weaken Virginia's belief in the existence of the wonderfully gentle, generous spirit she knew as Santa Claus. Christmas had always been a magic time, anticipation awakening with the first touch of fall. Santa Claus had never disappointed Virginia, but Santa had not been as apparent a spirit to all of her friends. Their disappointment took the form of disillusionment; and disillusionment gave way to doubt. There is no Santa Claus!

Virginia sought her father for advice. But here was a question requiring a more subtle answer than could readily be provided, and her father wisely deferred to greater authority. It was his habit to write the "Questions and Answers" column in the daily newspaper, *The Sun*. He advised Virginia to follow his example, "If you see it in *The Sun,* it's so." Post a letter to *The Sun?* Of Course!

Virginia's letter read:

Finally, on the 21st of September, the newspaper answered Virginia's letter, devoting an editorial to it.

The Sun had accepted a deeper challenge. Its editor gracefully and forcefully dealt with those mean souls and sour spirits who would declare the ultimate foolishness, "No Santa Claus!" Was there not more to Santa Claus than the purchases made for filling stockings on Christmas Eve? Didn't Santa Claus offer the stuff of more valuable gifts? Gifts for all seasons?

The letter that Virginia O'Hanlon sent to *The Sun* is undoubtedly the most widely read letter ever published in a newspaper. The editorial reply, by Francis Church, must undeniably be one of the most famous editorials in American journalism. It appeared in the very heart of the editorial page on Tuesday, September 21, 1897 entitled "Is There A Santa Claus." With its line, "Yes, Virginia. There Is A Santa Claus" both letter and editorial have taken their place in the annals of Americana and have spread their message through the entire world. *The Sun* reprinted the editorial each year prior to Christmas until 1949 when the paper published its last edition.

The Editorial read:

We take pleasure in answering at once and thus prominently the communication below, expressing at the same time our great gratification that its faithful author is numbered among the friends of *The Sun:*

Dear Editor:

I am 8 years old. Some of my little friends say there is no Santa Claus. Papa says "If you see it in *The Sun* It's so." Please tell me the truth; is there a Santa Claus?

VIRGINIA, your little friends are wrong. They have been affected by the skepticism of a skeptical age. They do not believe except they see. They think that nothing can be that is not comprehensible by their little minds.

All minds, VIRGINIA, whether they be men's or children's, are little. In this great universe of ours, man is a mere insect, an ant, in his intellect, as compared with the boundless world about him, as measured by the intelligence capable of grasping the whole truth and knowledge.

Yes, VIRGINIA, there is a Santa Claus. He exists as certainly as love and generosity and devotion exist,

and you know that they abound and give to your life its highest beauty and joy.

Alas! How dreary would be the world if there were no Santa Claus. It would be as dreary as if there were no VIRGINIAS.

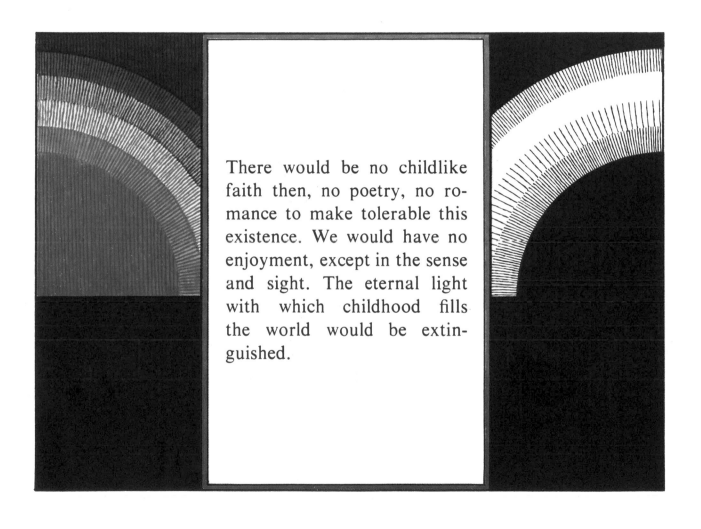

There would be no childlike faith then, no poetry, no romance to make tolerable this existence. We would have no enjoyment, except in the sense and sight. The eternal light with which childhood fills the world would be extinguished.

Not believe in Santa Claus! You might as well not believe in fairies! You might get your papa to hire men to watch in all the chimnies to catch Santa Claus on Christmas Eve, but even if they did not see Santa Claus coming down, what would that prove? Nobody sees Santa Claus but that is no sign that there is no Santa Claus.

Did you ever see fairies dancing on the lawn. Of course not, but that's no proof that they are not there. Nobody can conceive or imagine all the wonders there are unseen and unseeable in the world.

The most real things in the world are those that neither children nor men can see.

You may tear apart the baby's rattle and see what makes the noise inside, but there is a veil covering the unseen world which not the strongest man, nor even the united strength of all the strongest men that ever lived, could tear apart.

Only faith, fancy, poetry, love, romance, can push aside that curtain and view and picture the supernal beauty and glory beyond. Is it all real? Ah, VIRGINIA, in all this world there is nothing else real and abiding.

No Santa Claus! Thank God! he lives, and he lives forever. A thousand years from now, VIRGINIA, nay ten times ten thousand years from now, he will continue to make glad the heart of childhood.

Virginia, the only child of Philip P. O'Hanlon and Laura Lincoln Plumb O'Hanlon, grew up in New York City. She received a bachelors degree from Hunter College in 1910 and a masters degree from Columbia a year later. Virginia O'Hanlon worked with children all her life and at one time was principal of a school that held its classes in hospitals and other institutions for chronically ill children.

Philip P. O'Hanlon, the son and grandson of practicing physicians, himself practiced medicine in New York City his entire life. Educated at New York University, he served as coroner's physician from 1895 to 1911 and Police Surgeon from 1911 to 1932, returning to a pension and private practice in that year. He was a well-known diagnostician and neurologist. Dr. O'Hanlon died in 1937 at age 74.

Francis Pharcellus Church was son of a baptist minister and a lineal descendent of the Governor of the Massachusetts Colony. He graduated from Columbia College in 1859, studied law, and then took up writing. Francis Church was a war correspondent for the *New York Times* during the Civil War. He established the *Army and Navy Journal,* and *The Galaxy Magazine* which published some of the most noteworthy fiction and belles-lettres of the day. With the discontinuance of *The Galaxy,* Francis Church became an editorial writer for *The Sun.* He showed a determination to "examine and refine those grosser propositions which laziness and consent make current." He was an important editorial writer and a sculptor of note. Ironically, it was not until after his death in 1906 at age 67 that it became known that the response to Virginia O'Hanlon was indeed penned by him.

The Santa Claus of Virginia O'Hanlon and her times, and Santa Claus as we generally recognize him today, is the conception of Thomas Nast, who was possibly America's foremost political cartoonist. In the pages of Harpers Magazine for over a quarter of a century from the Civil War, and most famously in his book of "Christmas Drawings for the Human Race," Santa has evolved into the man with broad girth, captivating smile, and flowing white locks, moustache and beard.